4-50

THE ELVES AND THE SHOEMAKER

Words and Music by
MAURICE BAILEY

1. Once upon a time

For notes see page 32

OXFORD UNIVERSITY PRESS, MUSIC DEPARTMENT, WALTON STREET, OXFORD OX2 6DP

3. Every single day, people came from miles around
To that little Shoemaker –once upon a time!

4. They would come to choose pairs of shiny boots and shoes,
To that little Shoemaker –once upon a time!

NARRATOR: The Shoemaker sat at his bench all day, working the leather into shoes. While he did so, his wife would be busy doing the cleaning and cooking. At mid-day, she would bring him some food and wine, and he would stop work long enough to eat and drink it.

2. Here's some bread

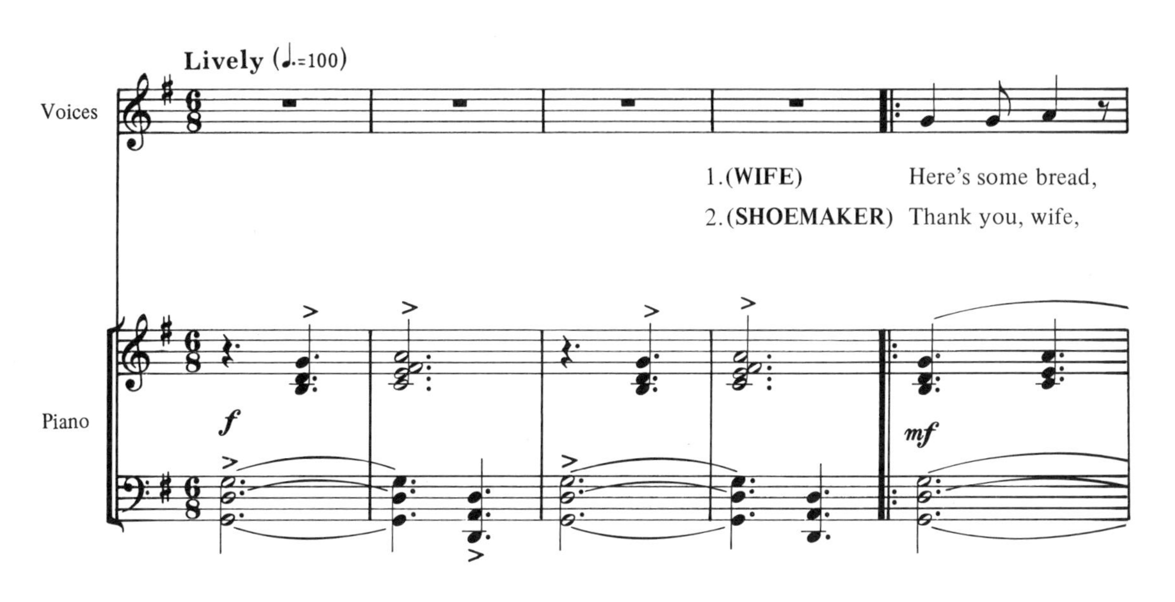

10
Stop your work, eat and drink, But
Work - ing cares I will shed, And
mf
15
don't for-get to wash your hands –
as I eat your home-baked bread
I've put some wat - er in the
I bless the day that we were
19
Triangles
mf
sink! (The Shoemaker washes his hands, while his wife places the food on the table. He sits down to eat.)
wed! (He finishes his meal, then returns to his work.)
f
mf

24
Cymbals
Drums and/or Tamboutines
f
f
f
29
Triangles
mf
mf
35
Cymbals
Drums/Tambourines
f
f
f
mf
mf dim.
41
1.
2.
p
p
pp

NARRATOR: As soon as he had finished eating and drinking, the Shoemaker would return to his work, and, sometimes, as he worked, he would sing a little song to himself. It went like this:

3. Stitch, stitch, stitch

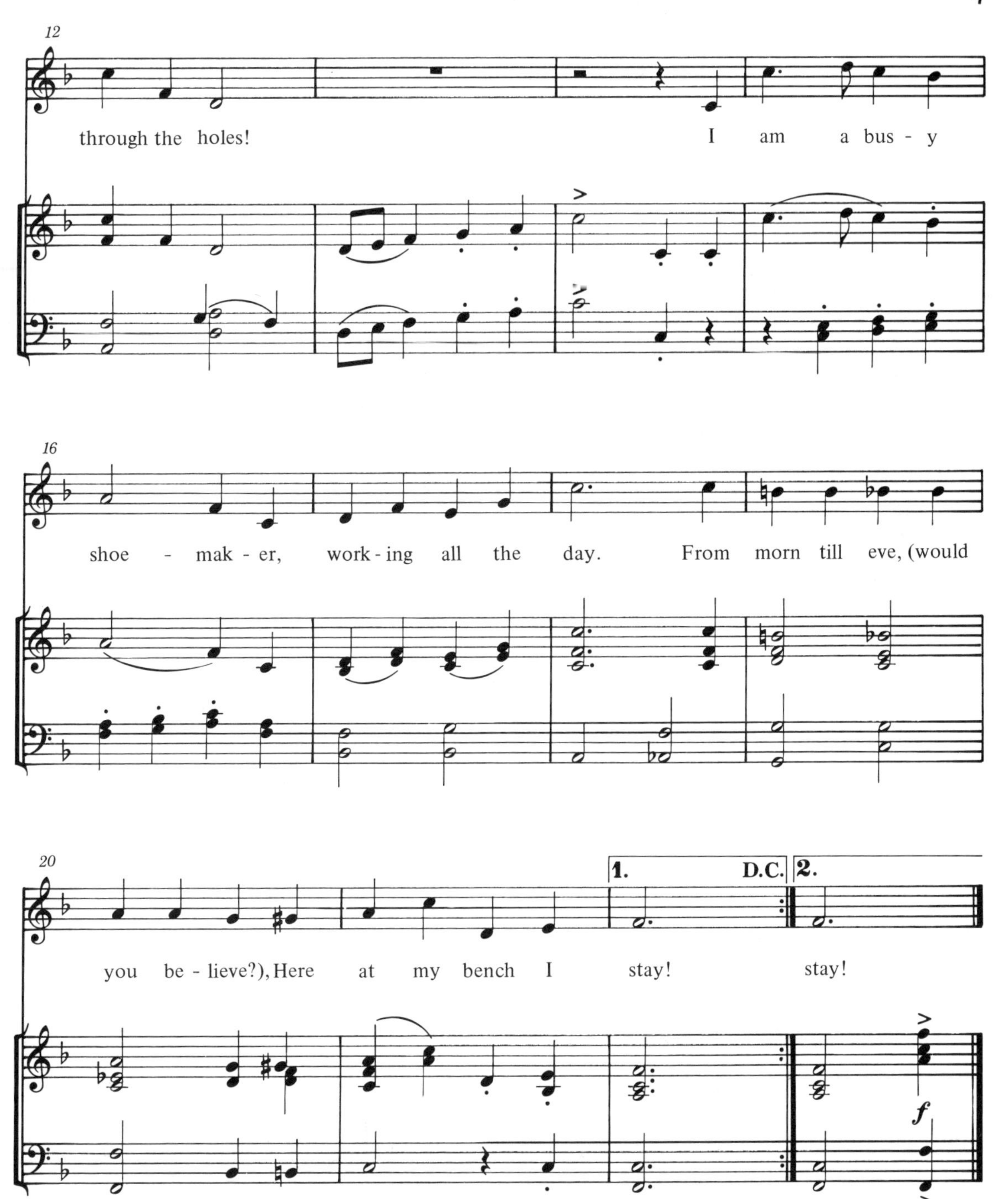

2. Stitch, stitch, stitch, the whole day through –
Time to start another shoe!
Then I'll have a brand new pair
For a gentleman to wear!
I am a busy shoemaker, working all the day.
From morn to eve, (would you believe?),
Here at my bench I stay!

NARRATOR: Although the Shoemaker made lots of pairs of shoes, he did not make very much money. Often, people would come into his shop, look at the shoes, and then offer him far less money than the shoes were really worth. Then the Shoemaker, thinking that he might not sell the shoes at all, would agree to sell them at a price that would hardly pay for the leather. Here comes somebody to buy a pair of shoes now!

4. I think these shoes are not too good

2. These heels for me are much too high,
Perhaps another pair I'll buy!
But you have nothing else to suit.
For I don't want a clumsy boot,
For I don't want a clumsy boot!

3. Although the workmanship is bad
I do not like to see you sad,
And so, because I'm very nice
I'll buy them – but at half your price,
I'll buy them – but at half your price!

NARRATOR: One day, after the Shoemaker had sold a pair of shoes, he had only enough leather left to make one more pair, and not enough money to buy any more leather. How could he and his wife afford to live if he could not sell any more shoes?

He called his wife, and told her the problem. She said, 'You are very tired. Cut out the leather, but do not make the shoes today. Perhaps we shall think of something in the morning!'

So the Shoemaker cut out the leather, and left it on his bench. Then he and his wife went off to bed.

5. Sleep tight

NARRATOR: Soon they were so fast asleep that they did not hear the church clock chime twelve o'clock – or what happened afterwards! We shall have to keep very still and quiet, too, or else we may frighten the little elves away!

5a. Entry of the Elves

(*The Elves work in silence, stitching the leather into a pair of shoes. When they finish, they place the shoes on the bench, and run out of the shop. When they have gone, No.5b is played softly under the narration.*)

5b. Sleeping music

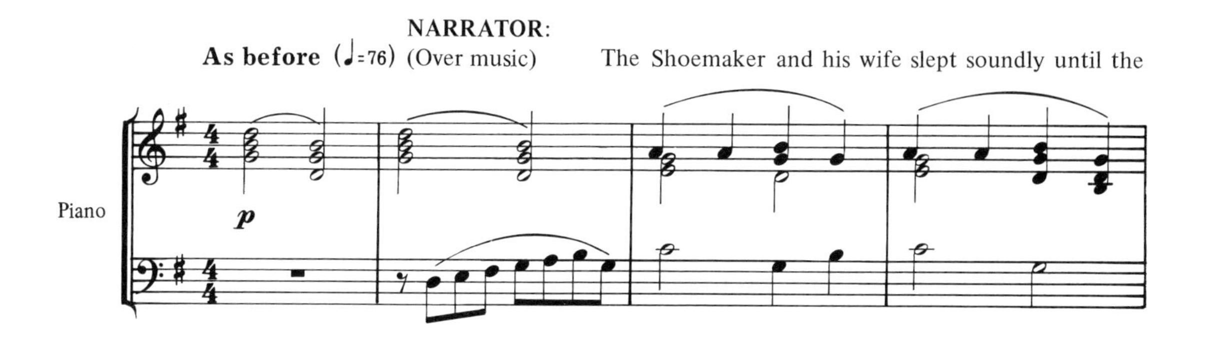

church clock struck seven the next morning.

They did not know that, while they were asleep, the little elves

had stitched the leather into a beautiful pair of shoes!

NARRATOR: At seven o'clock they woke up, rubbed the sleep from their eyes, and got out of bed. Sadly, the Shoemaker went to look at his last piece of leather, wondering what he would do, now that he could afford to buy no more. Instead of the leather, he saw a pair of finished shoes. He could hardly believe his eyes! He called his wife, and she looked at them as well.

6. Oh! What a lovely piece of footwear!

17
ver - y fun - ny, (No more bread and no more hon - ey!), Some-one came while
p cresc.
21
we were sleep - ing, From our one re - main - ing piece of leath - er,
mf
25
[1st time D.C.]
Fash - ioned such a love - ly pair of shoes!
29
f

NARRATOR: Soon a lady entered. She looked at the shoes, picked them up, and tried one on. She liked them very much.

7. I think these shoes are very good!

2. These shoes are quite the best I've seen
Although to many shops I've been.
The colour's right – they suit me well,
I'd like to buy if you will sell,
I'd like to buy if you will sell!

3. The workmanship is really fine,
the leather has a lovely shine!
And so, because the shoes are nice,
I'll pay you quite a goodly price,
I'll pay you quite a goodly price!

NARRATOR: The lady gave the Shoemaker so much money, that he had enough to buy leather for *two* more pairs of shoes, and money over to give to his wife to buy food.

(*The next three paragraphs of the narrative are not mimed.* ***The Shoemaker*** *stays at his bench, working, while* ***his wife*** *is busy doing the housework.*)

NARRATOR: He cut out the leather for two new pairs of shoes, but he did not start to make them at once. He decided to stitch them in the morning. However, when he got up the next day, there, on the bench, were two pairs of beautifully-made shoes!

This time a gentleman came into the shop and liked the shoes so much that he bought both pairs, paying so much money that the Shoemaker had enough to buy leather for *four* more pairs of shoes, and money over to give to his wife to buy food.

Every night after that, the Shoemaker left more and more leather cut out on his bench, and, every morning, he would find perfectly made shoes. He sold every pair at such a good price that he soon became rich.

(*The mime now continues in detail*)

NARRATOR: But the Shoemaker and his wife often wondered who the secret workmen were. One night, instead of going to bed, they hid behind a curtain, and waited to see what would happen. As the church clock struck twelve, two little elves entered . . . .

8. Elves' entrance and work music

(They start to stitch the leather)
24
♩=168 (𝅗𝅥.=56)
mp
Xylos.
mp
Glocks.(or Chime Bars)
(Triangles and Tamboúrines)
Triangles
mp
mp
29
(Triangles)
mf
cresc.
mf
35
mf
p
mf
(Triangles)
mf
p
mf

40
Tambourines
(Glocks.)
p
p
p cresc.
46
Glocks.
mp
mp
51
dim.
dim.
56
pp
pp

NARRATOR: The elves worked so fast that they had finished all the shoes in hardly any time at all. Yet, when the elves had gone, and the Shoemaker and his wife came to look, they saw that the shoes were as beautifully made as ever.

The Shoemaker said, 'We must try to find a way of thanking the elves – after all, they have made us rich!' So they thought for a long time. Suddenly, his wife said, 'I know! Let us make them some nice clothes! Although they make the shoes so well, their clothes are very old and ragged!'

The next morning, it was market day. The Shoemaker's wife decided to go and buy material for the clothes. While she was out, the Shoemaker took the softest leather he could find to make each elf a pair of shoes. When his wife arrived at the market, she looked round all the stalls carefully, until she saw just the material she wanted.

9. At the market

7
At the mar - ket! There are lots of
Drums
mf
There are bags and
Pears and plums and
Cymbals
10
things of val - ue If you want to
leath - er cas - es
lo - gan - ber - ries
Drums
Cymbals
13
buy!
mf
Xylophones

NARRATOR: Having bought just the right material, she returned home, and, while her husband was finishing the shoes, she set to work to make shirts, jackets and trousers for their tiny visitors.

10. We are a busy couple

2. Making shirts, and trousers too,
Lovely jackets, new as new!
Little shoes to fit their feet,
In these clothes they'll look so neat!
We are a busy couple, not working for ourselves,
We'll toil all day just to repay those clever little elves!

NARRATOR: They worked all day until the evening. When all the clothes were eventually finished, the Shoemaker's wife laid them out on the bench in place of the usual leather. She and her husband hoped they would fit!

Then they hid once more behind the curtain to watch what would happen. Again, nothing did until the church clock struck twelve.

(The first twenty-three bars of No. 8 can be played while ***the Shoemaker*** *and* ***his wife*** *hide, the clock strikes twelve, and* ***the elves*** *enter. Then there is silence as* ***the elves*** *are puzzled at first to see the clothes on the bench. But when they realise to their delight that the clothes are meant for them to wear, they gleefully put them on and dance round the room to the music of No. 11. By the end of the music, they have left the shop, danced their way along the road, and are out of sight.)*

11. Dance

11

(Glock.1)

15

(Glock.2)

19 (Glock.1)

(Glock.2)

23
(Glock.1)
27
(Glock.2)
31
8

NARRATOR: The Shoemaker and his wife were so delighted with what they had seen, that they were up at first light the next morning. They were too excited to eat any breakfast! The Shoemaker said: 'Let's try to remember how the elves danced when they wore their new clothes!' And so they started to dance. Their neighbours, seeing them dancing so happily first thing in the morning, joined in, and soon the whole village was dancing! Even the elves came back and joined in, but no one noticed!

REPEAT NO. 11 – DANCE

NARRATOR: At the end of the dance, the villagers returned to their business, and the Shoemaker went back to his bench to start the day's work. The elves were never seen again, but the Shoemaker had no cause to worry. He was now rich and famous, and could sell all the shoes he made at a good price. But he and his wife never forgot the little men who, by making such perfect shoes, had done them such a good turn!

And, as he worked, the Shoemaker would sometimes sing a little song to himself. It went like this:

12. Stitch, stitch, stitch

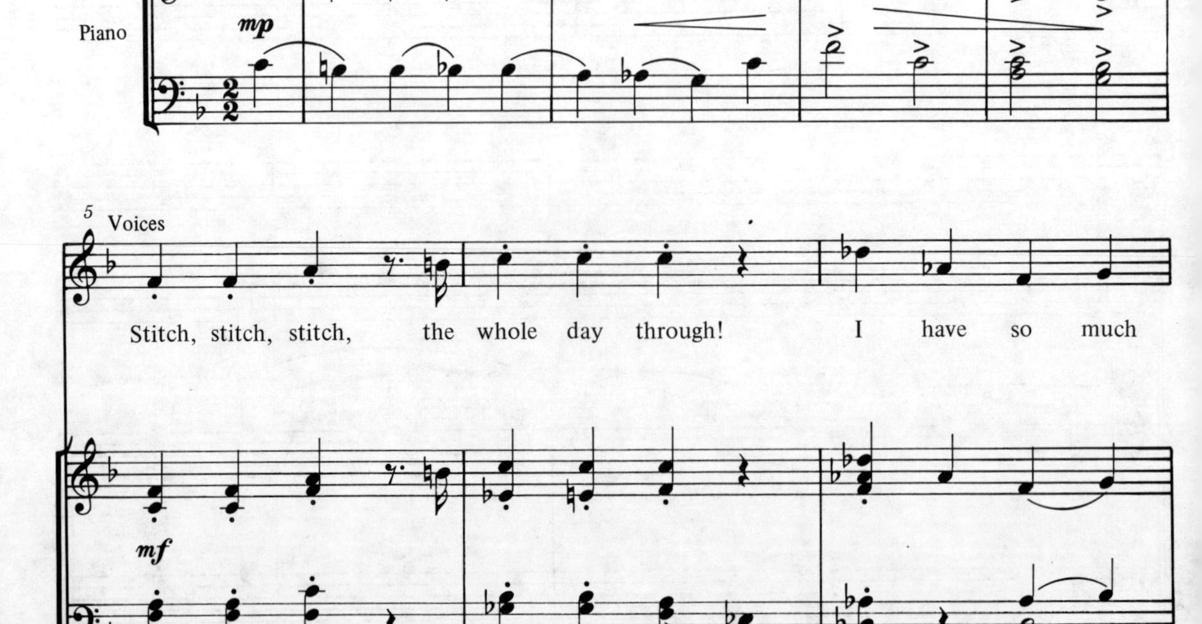

Reproduced and printed by Halstan & Co. Ltd., Amersham, Bucks., England

Characters
The Shoemaker, his wife, first customer, second (lady) customer, two elves, market stall-holders, villagers

Instrumental parts
Piano (adult performer)
Descant recorders (using G to D′ only) *optional*
Tuned and untuned percussion *optional*

The story is told and sung by children. The operetta is suitable for Lower Juniors.

A separate recorder/percussion part is on sale.

Duration 35 minutes

Notes for performance

1. Groups of children may share the narration, while actors mime the story.

2. Most of the action takes place in the Shoemaker's workshop, which also serves as a living-room. A workbench is in evidence, preferably with a hidden shelf underneath from which pairs of 'newly-made' shoes can be produced during the course of the story. There may be a separate bedroom or just a door from the workshop ostensibly leading to a bedroom, through which the Shoemaker and his wife may retire when required.

3. The market scene can provide activities for a large number of children if desired.

4. The singers and percussionists should sit surrounding and facing the house and market, with the recorder players grouped near the piano.

5. The stall-holders can join in the singing throughout. Everybody takes part in the general dance (repeat of No. 11).

6. The recorder and percussion parts are optional. Alternatively additional percussion parts may be added.